1

Photocopiable activities for

Language and Literacy

Irene Yates

Author
Irene Yates

Editor
Sally Gray

Assistant editor
Clare Miller

Series designer
Joy White

Designer
Sarah Rock

Illustrations
Jenny Tulip

Cover photo
Martyn Chillmaid

Published by Scholastic Ltd, Villiers House, Clarendon Avenue,
Leamington Spa, Warwickshire CV32 5PR

© 1998 Scholastic Ltd   Text © 1998 Irene Yates
2 3 4 5 6 7 8 9 0   9 0 1 2 3 4 5 6 7

British Library Cataloguing-in-Publication Data
A catalogue record for this book is available from the British Library.

ISBN 0-590-53880-2

Contents

Introduction

All children begin their pre-school groups with some knowledge of language. The language they have is the language that they speak and hear at home with people they are familiar with. The children in your group will come to you with varying degrees of language ability. But whatever their ability it must be respected and utilized as the foundation from which all further language development will take place.

Language development is the key to the intellectual, social and emotional life of each child and can be considered the most important Area of Learning when they move into school. All the key areas of the Desirable Outcomes for children's learning are greatly dependent upon the cultivation of efficient communication skills.

The Desirable Outcomes for Language and Literacy

In this book you will find a range of activities to provide coverage of all the areas of the Language and Literacy curriculum specified by the School Curriculum and Assessment Authority in their publication *Desirable Outcomes for Children's Learning*. The ideas can also be applied equally well to the pre-school curriculum guidance documents for Wales, Scotland and Northern Ireland.

The Desirable Outcomes for Language and Literacy split the development of good communication skills into three specific areas:

- Speaking and listening;
- Enjoying books and reading;
- Writing.

Of course, when the children are engaged in an activity from any of these areas they may be practising skills in the other areas. For example a child who is talking about something they have heard, seen or done, is putting together a kind of story; is learning about listening from the listener and is developing confidence in speaking. The chapters in this book each concentrate on a different aspect of the Language and Literacy curriculum, covering the specific areas detailed above in a comprehensive way as well as providing suggestions for ways to extend and adapt the activities to meet the needs of all the children in your care.

Using the photocopiable activities

Within each chapter you will find photocopiable activity sheets with notes to help you make the most of each activity. The sheets can be used with different-sized groups though it helps to remember that each child will need some individual attention, particularly with the writing sheets. Allow all the children to work at their own level of development, always encouraging them to try just a little bit more each time. Use some of the sheets as evidence of attainment to store in the children's personal portfolios.

Enlarge some of the sheets to A3-size to enhance the activity or to help children with visual discrimination and/or less developed fine motor skills. Many of the activities can also be used as a template to be adapted and repeated many times.

Use lots of resources

Try to use the activity sheets with the children in the context of your own group — you may find that creating a café area or shop, for example, will help the children to get more benefit from the writing activities. Role-play is a useful tool for language learning. The children learn to use language that is not their 'norm' by 'becoming' someone else; they also learn empathy and consideration of other people's feelings. Many of the sheets offer the opportunity for further reinforcement games and play, simply by backing them to card and/or laminating them. Others require the

use of additional resources such as collage and colouring materials. The use of a wide range of resources, in itself, provides opportunities for language development.

The more the children use the activities in their normal 'play' and learning context, the more they will learn from them. For example, there are several activities that require the children to make their own simple books. Try not to let this kind of activity begin and end with the making. Encourage the children to build their own little book corner in the play area, help them to role-play situations such as pretending to be mummy or daddy putting teddy to bed and reading a story with them beforehand. This kind of play will promote a good attitude towards books and reading, reinforcing the work at the group and the good practice that you hope they are experiencing at home.

Home links

You will find that the children will be very happy to take their sheets home to show their friends and families what they have achieved. Encourage this practice and also try to involve the parents or carers in explanations of why you are doing the activities. Take as many opportunities as you can to involve them in the children's development. Take time to explain how they might use the material at home to further their child's learning, by encouraging them to talk to their child about what they have done. It can also be very beneficial to let the children take some of the sheets home to complete with their parents or carers. This will help to involve the parents even more and you can arrange follow-up discussions with them when the activity sheets are returned.

About this series

The *Learning in the Early Years* series comprises two sets of books. The first set of seven books (one for each of the Desirable Outcomes and a series handbook, *Ready for Inspection*) each contain sections on child development, planning, assessment and record-keeping, activity ideas and photocopiable resources. The second series of books, designed to reinforce and develop the ideas in the first series of books, comprises six books packed full of new and exciting photocopiable activity ideas to comprehensively cover the Desirable Outcomes for learning:

* Language and Literacy
* Mathematics
* Personal and Social Development
* Knowledge and Understanding of the World
* Creative Development
* Physical Development.

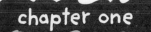
Talking and listening

In this chapter the children will be encouraged to think about what listening means and to put into words and express what they hear. They will have opportunities to speak in small groups and to exchange ideas with adults and other children.

PAGE 9

Tell what you see

Learning objective

To identify, name and describe objects and events.

What to do

Work with individuals, pairs or three children. Look at the illustrations together and ask them specific questions about each one, such as: What is this? What can you see? Tell me about it. Ask each child to colour the pictures, cut them out and stick them on a page. Write the name of the person, place or thing underneath.

PAGE 10

What do you hear?

Learning objective

To identify, name and describe sounds.

What to do

Work with individuals or small groups. Point out the objects, one at a time. Ask each child to name the objects. Does it make a noise? What kind of noise does it make? Can you change the noise? Try to make a noise like it.

If possible find objects in the room to correspond with the pictures and listen to their sounds. Extend the idea by asking the children to find three objects that make different sounds, describe them and then draw them.

PAGE 11

Shopping day

Learning objective

To observe and discuss a picture of a familiar activity.

What to do

Work with individuals or small groups. Ask each child to tell you what they can see in the picture. Ask: What is this? What are they doing? What do you think they will buy? Let each child cut round the picture and stick it to card.

Can they tell you about when they go shopping? Ask them to choose something for you to write under their picture. Make a display of the children's shopping cards and sentences.

Where are the bears?

PAGE 12

Learning objective

To observe and use positional words for location.

What to do

Work with individuals. Ask the child to point out all the bears they can see in the picture. Ask them to tell you what each bear is doing and where it is. Help them to use positional language by prompting them with questions such as: Is there a bear behind/beside/under anything? Encourage the child to colour

the picture and then make up sentences for you to write onto a piece of paper. Stick the coloured sheet and the writing onto a piece of A3 paper and fold to make into a booklet. Read the child's words back to them.

Penguin pictures
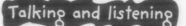

Learning objective

To recognize and verbalize different movement actions.

What to do

Work with individuals or pairs. Look at the pictures together. Ask the children to find a penguin doing each of the actions – rolling, pushing, carrying and throwing. What is happening in each picture? Can they think of some other things that you can throw/roll/push/carry?

Which could you hear?

Learning objective

To recognize and categorize familiar objects.

What to do

Work with up to three children. Explain that the picture shows some things that make sounds and some which do not. Ask them to point out the things they think *don't* make sounds and then the things they think do. What noises do those things make? Can they describe the noise in words? Help the children to use words such as quiet, silent, loud and noisy. Ask the children to think of five more noisy things and five silent things. Make a group book of noisy and silent things, using the pictures from the sheet as a starting point.

What's happening?

Learning objective

To recognize and describe different activities.

What to do

Work with individual children. Ask each child to describe the actions they can see in the pictures. What jobs are being done? Look at the pictures one at a time and invite the child to talk through what's happening and who the characters in the pictures might be. Mime some other household activities for the children to guess. Encourage

them to use some play equipment to role-play the various household chores.

Make a rhyme

PAGE 16

Learning objective

To identify words that rhyme.

What to do

Work with individual children. Encourage them to find two words to rhyme with 'cat'. Give each child an activity sheet and help them to fill in the missing letters, reinforcing the words several times.

Use the same format to work with other word rhymes such as, big/pig/dig or van/man/can. Make a group rhyme book by working on different word families and assembling all the children's work together to make a book. Send the book home with individual children and encourage the parents to read it with them.

How many sounds?

PAGE 17

Learning objective

To identify objects that will make sounds, and to describe those sounds.

What to do

Work with two or three children. Talk about the picture. What can they see happening? Invite them to describe each of the objects and activities. Ask them to find something in the picture that would be making a noise. Can they name the object or activity? What words such as 'tinkle' or 'crash', would describe the noise? Let the children choose one of the pictures to write a word, phrase or sentence about.

Odd word out

PAGE 18

Learning objective

To identify and name objects and to identify rhyming words.

What to do

Work with individuals. Take a section at a time and ask the child to identify each picture in the section, saying the four words clearly as they point to the objects. Point out that three of the words have the same sound – they rhyme – and that one sounds different. Ask the children to identify the non-rhyming word, then reinforce it by asking them the rhyming words.

Tell what you see

Talk about these pictures.

What do you hear?

What sounds do these things make?

Shopping day

Talk about the picture.

Where are the bears?

Talk about what the bears are doing.

Penguin pictures

What are the penguins doing?

Which could you hear?

Which of these things make a noise?

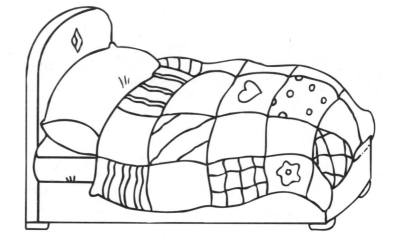

What's happening?

Talk about what you can see.

Make a rhyme

Fill in the missing letters and draw the pictures.

cat
hat
mat

cat

h _ _

m _ _

How many sounds?

Talk about all the things you can see.

What sounds would you hear?

Odd word out

Say the words.

Listen to the sounds.

Learning in the Early Years - Photocopiable Activities

Language and Literacy

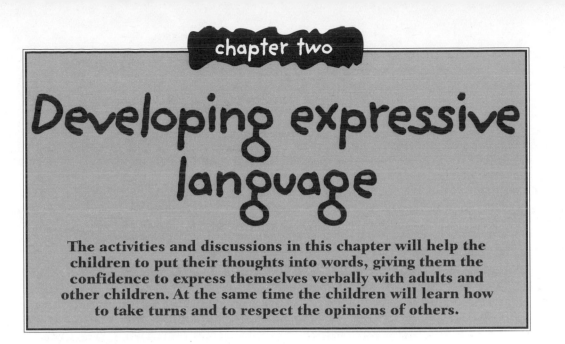

chapter two

Developing expressive language

The activities and discussions in this chapter will help the children to put their thoughts into words, giving them the confidence to express themselves verbally with adults and other children. At the same time the children will learn how to take turns and to respect the opinions of others.

PAGE 21

What do they do?
Learning objective
To identify and describe people.
What to do
Work with individuals or small groups. Look at each illustration with the children and ask them to say what each one shows. What are they doing? Where are they going? Have you met someone like this? Ask the children to name the objects at the bottom of the sheet and say what they are for. Let them cut out the pictures of the people and the objects and ask them to match them up, sticking the object next to the appropriate person on a piece of paper.

PAGE 22

Make a story
Learning objective
To create and verbalize a story, following a sequence.
What to do
Work with individuals or pairs. Demonstrate that the sequence of each story goes from left to right, following the arrows. Help them to describe the pictures by asking them questions. What can you see? What's happening?

If we were telling the story, what would we say?
Let the child choose one of the sequences and make a book. Scribe the words for the child, or allow them to have a go themselves.

Where are the toys?
PAGE 23
Learning objective
To use positional words.
What to do
Work with a small group. Look at the picture together. Invite the children to take turns to talk about the picture and to identify the objects at the bottom of the page. Explain to the children that you want them to tell you where these objects are in the picture, but not by saying 'there'. They must describe where the objects are, for example 'next to the door'. How many ways can they find to describe each object?

How do they feel?
PAGE 24
Learning objective
To recognize, describe and express emotions and feelings.
What to do
Work with individuals. Show each child

the faces on the page. Help them to describe how the people are feeling. Invite each child to choose a 'face', cut it out and stick it to a paper bag, to make a puppet. Can they make their puppet talk and behave in a manner to suit its face? Encourage the children to perform puppet shows for each other.

What are they for?

PAGE 25

Learning objective
To identify, name and describe some objects.
What to do
Work with two or three children. Enlarge a copy of the activity sheet and look at and talk about the pictures together. Invite the children to take turns to describe what they can see in the individual pictures, giving as much detail as possible. Make two copies of the sheet onto card, ask pairs of children to colour the cards identically and use them for a game of Snap.

A busy park

PAGE 26

Learning objective
To observe, identify, describe and talk about a picture.
What to do
Work with individuals. Invite the child to tell you exactly what they can see. Encourage them to look very closely at the picture and ask them lots of questions to stimulate ideas. Colour and cut out parts of the picture. Look in magazines and catalogues for more outdoors pictures. Stick all the collected pieces to a big sheet of sugar paper for a group 'At the park' montage. Encourage the children to talk about their contribution to the montage and the other things that they can see on it.

Whatever next?

PAGE 27

Learning objective
To make observations and predictions.
What to do
Work with individuals or pairs. Look at the pictures one at a time and ask the child to tell you about the picture, naming objects and describing events. What do they think will happen next? Why? How could they stop it from happening? Can they think of a

different ending? Together, think up a situation where something is going to happen, discuss and draw the situation. Encourage the child to ask a friend 'What will happen next?'

Make up the story

PAGE 28

Learning objective
To create and verbalize a story.
What to do
Work with small groups of children and ask them to talk about the dragon picture with you. Ask them: Who do you think the child might be? Where has the dragon come from? Where is it going to? What will happen next? Write down the children's ideas and invite them to draw pictures to go with their dragon stories. Make the stories into little books to share with friends and families.

Who's this?

PAGE 29

Learning objective
To recognize and name body parts.
What to do
Work with individuals. Enlarge a copy of the activity sheet to A3-size and invite the child to look at the picture, describing what they can see. Ask them to name each body part individually (using vocabulary such as 'paws'). Let the child cut the parts out and put teddy together again by sticking the pieces together on a separate piece of paper, naming each part as they go. Stick the bear pictures to paper bags to make puppets. Let the children take their puppets home to tell their families what happened to the teddy.

Things we do

PAGE 30

Learning objective
To talk about everyday activities.
What to do
Work with individual children. Ask them to describe each of the activities they can see. Ask them: Do you do this at home? Do you help with this? Invite the children to cut out the pictures, sequence them to show a typical day and stick them in their chosen order on paper or in a small home-made book. Encourage more able children to write some words underneath.

What do they do?

Who are these people? How do they help us?

Make a story

Look at the pictures. Talk about what is happening.

Where are the toys?

Find these toys in the picture. Can you describe where they are?

Learning in the Early Years - Photocopiable Activities

Language and Literacy

How do they feel?

Talk about the faces.

What are they for?

Name these things. What are they for?

A busy park

Look at the picture carefully. Talk about what you can see.

Whatever next?

What do you think will happen next?

Make up the story

Talk about what you can see.

Make up your own story.

Who's this?

Do you know who this is? Name all the body parts.

Things we do

Talk about what is happening in the pictures.

chapter three

Developing early reading skills

The activities in this chapter will encourage the development of aural and visual discrimination and memory, help the children to acquire left to right orientation skills and encourage them in shape, letter and word matching.

PAGE 33

Bear games
Learning objective
To observe similarities of shape, pattern and size.
What to do
Work with individuals. Look at the illustrations and count the bears together. Ask the child to look at the bears closely and find all the sets of bears that are the same. Help them to draw lines between the sets. Ask them to explain what makes the bears the same. Stick three sets of the bears to card, colour them and cut them out. Let pairs of children play 'Bear Snap'.

PAGE 34

Match the fish
Learning objective
To observe similarities of shape, pattern, size and direction.
What to do
Work with individuals. Ask the child to observe all the fish on the sheet and tell you about them, describing the patterns. Invite the child to draw lines to matching fish. Ask the child to draw and describe two more fish, the same as each other but different from the others on the sheet.

PAGE 35

Colourful clowns
Learning objective
To observe differences in shape and pattern.
What to do
Work with individuals. Ask the child to look closely at the clowns, deciding which one is different from the others. In what ways is it different? Ask the child to draw a clown the same as the odd one out in the box.

PAGE 36

Left to right
Learning objective
To practise left to right orientation skills.
What to do
Work with small groups. Help the children to 'read' the page by identifying the objects at the beginning and end of each line. Do they notice that the squiggly lines between the objects are all different and that they all go from the left of the page to the right? Encourage each child to trace their fingers carefully over the lines in the right direction. Now let each child trace the same lines from left to right in the sand tray.

Match the letters
Learning objective
To match letters.
What to do
Work with individual children. Show the child the page with all the triangles on. Take each triangle in turn and ask the child to read and identify the letter in the point and then to join it to the same letter on the opposite side. Help them to read all the letters and make the corresponding letter sounds. Use this format to teach children specific letters that they need to reinforce.

Find the letters
Learning objective
To identify and match letters.
What to do
Work with individuals. Ask the child to draw a line from the letter in the middle of the circle to the letter or letters it matches around the edge. Help the child to identify the middle letter first and then move clockwise round the circle to find the matching letters.

Begins with 'b'
Learning objective
To identify objects that begin with the 'b' sound.
What to do
Work with small groups. Provide each child with a sheet and ask them to trace round the letter 'b' in the box. Look at each picture in turn and ask individual children to tell you what each object is. Ask the children to say the word together and decide if it starts with a 'b' sound. The children can write the letter under each object (or try to write the word if they are more confident). Reinforce the formation of the letter 'b' and its sound each time.

Doing the dusting
Learning objective
To identify and name objects that begin with the sound 'd'.
What to do
Work with small groups. Make a 'd' shape in the air and ask the children to copy you. Give each child an activity sheet and help them to write the letter in the box. Look at the pictures together and ask the children to find the things that begin with the letter 'd'. Invite more able children to try to write the 'd' words on the back of the sheet.

Circle the letter
Learning objective
To look for, observe and identify letters within words.
What to do
Work with individuals. Look at the letters down the left hand side of the activity sheet. Help the child to identify and name them. Now look at the rows of words in turn. Remind the child which letter they are looking for. Read each word carefully and slowly to the child, letting your finger move in a left to right direction along it. Ask the child to point out the letter they're looking for and to draw a circle around it (or them).

Read the word again, emphasizing where the letter sound is. Use this format to teach any letters the children are having problems with.

Word snap
Learning objective
To look for, observe and identify words within groups of words.
What to do
Work with individual children who are beginning to read. With the child, look at the words down the left hand side of the sheet and help the child to read them. Point out the row of words alongside each word. Remind the child which word they are looking for in each line. Help the child to read each word and to draw a circle around the right word.

Use this format to teach the child words they need to learn. Send home sheets like this to practise and reinforce skills.

Bear games

Which bears are the same?

Match the fish.

Join each fish to the one that is exactly the same.

Draw two fish that match each other.

Colourful clowns

Draw a circle round the odd one out.

Draw a clown
in the box to
match the
one in
your circle.

Left to right

Trace the line from each toy to the place it wants to go.

Match the letters

In each triangle match the letters that are the same.

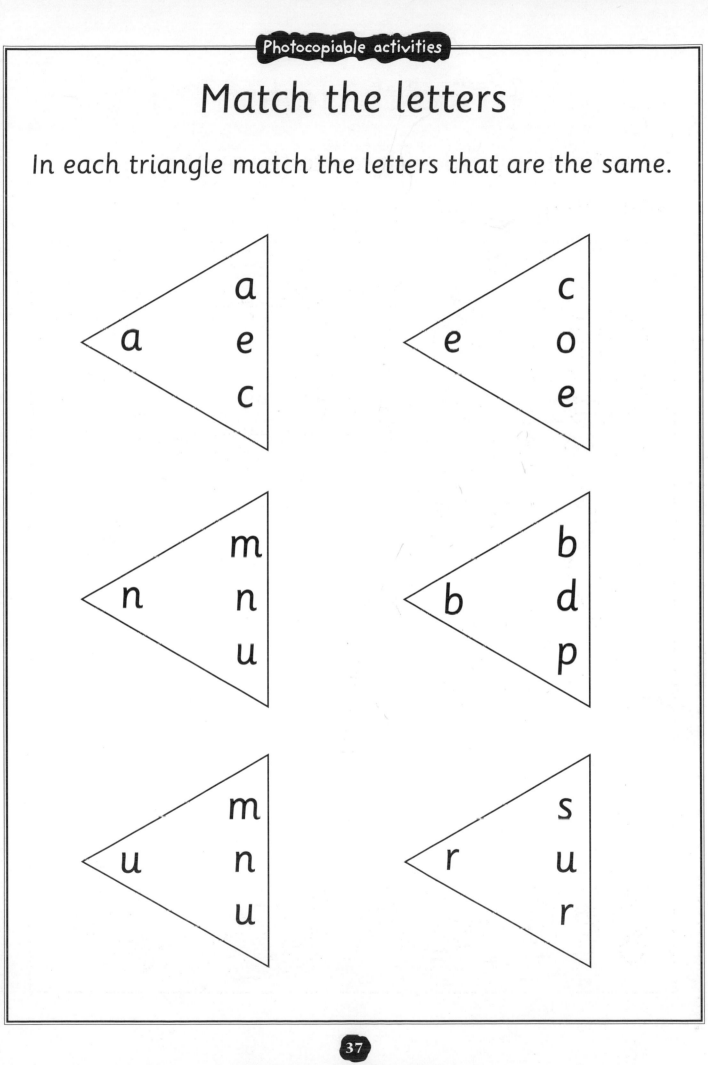

Find the letters

Draw a line to each letter in the circle that matches the letter in the middle.

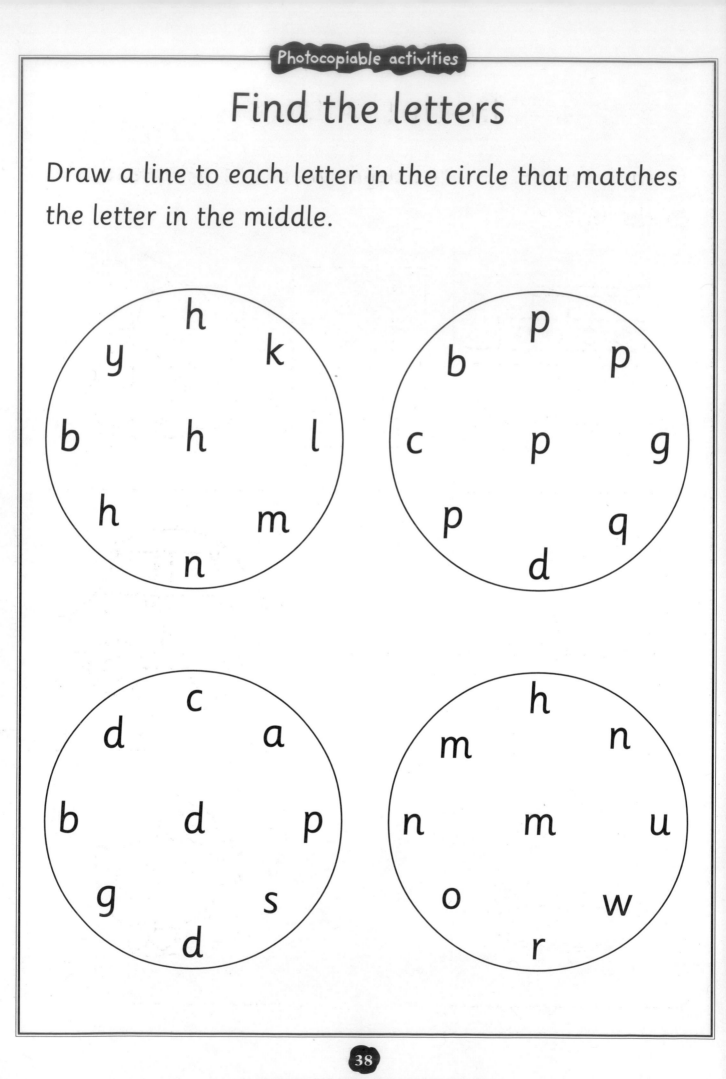

Begins with 'b'

Colour the things that begin with a 'b'. Write a 'b' in the box.

Doing the dusting

Colour the things that begin with 'd'. Write a 'd' in the box.

Circle the letter

Put a circle round the letters that are the same as the one at the beginning of each line.

t	tub	paint	butter	what
n	not	new	none	bun
u	uncle	run	up	put
h	high	when	ship	school
g	egg	go	green	big
o	top	do	brown	cook

Word snap

Put a circle round the word that is the same in each line.

dog	bin	dog	go	boy
me	them	you	me	we
come	go	now	make	come
cat	pat	cot	tock	cat
we	we	me	weed	am
happy	hop	happy	poppy	map

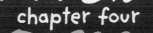

chapter four

Sharing books

The activities in this chapter provide a number of different starting points for sharing books. When children share books from an early age they learn that reading is an enjoyable experience. In addition they learn how stories, pages and print work, and they are motivated to want to learn to read.

PAGE 45

Flap book
Learning objective
To make a simple book to share.
What to do
Demonstrate this activity to a small group and then work with individuals on the task. Cut along the dotted lines and fold the solid lines on the activity sheet. The first two pages of the 'book' have pictures on them; ask the child to decide what to put on the remaining two pages. Write on the outside flap, what is underneath it. Fold the finished book and reinforce with sticky tape along the top edge. Write the title and child's name on the front.

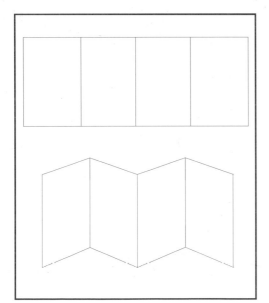

PAGE 46

What's the story?
Learning objective
To make a book of a well-known story.
What to do
Work with small groups. Ask the children to look carefully at the pictures and decide what is happening in each one. Make up a caption for each picture and tell them. Do they recognise the

story? Give each child a copy of the sheet and help them to cut out the frames. For each child fold two sheets of paper inside each other to make a small book. Secure with a staple. Ask the child to stick the pictures in the correct order. Help them to write their own sentence under each picture. On the front of the book write the title of the story and 'Retold by (child's name)'. Share the books with the rest of the group.

Tell the story
PAGE 47
Learning objective
To make up a story from a sequence of pictures.
What to do
Work with individual children. Ask the child to look at the pictures with you and describe what is happening in each one. Cut the pictures out and stick them to small sheets of paper. Arrange the pages in the right order and ask the child to give you a sentence to write for each picture. Ask the child to make up a title and write this and the child's name onto a title page. Staple the pages together to make a book. Encourage the child to share the book with friends and family.

Butterfly
PAGE 48
Learning objective
To make a simple pop-up book.
What to do
Work with individuals and provide each child with an activity sheet and a plain piece of paper. Let the child colour in the butterfly. Fold the centre fold line and cut along the lines indicated. Glue the sides of the butterfly to the piece of paper. Fold the two pieces of paper to

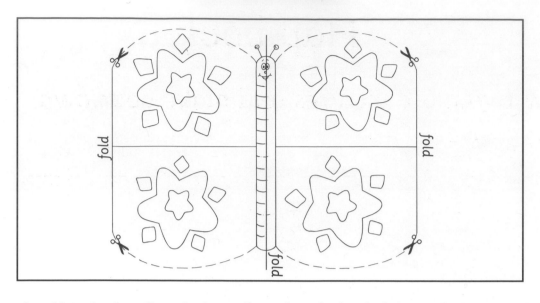

close like a book, pulling the butterfly shape out towards you. Open the book and the butterfly will pop out (see above). Help the child to write a butterfly story around the edges of the inner page.

My favourite things
PAGE 49

Learning objective
To make a colour picture book.
What to do
Work with small groups. Look at the activity sheet together as you read the title and the words to them. Give each child a sheet and as you read out the colour names again help them to make a mark in the appropriate colour in each box. Ask them to think of something they like in each colour and to draw it in its relevant box.

Cut out the children's pictures and stick each one onto a sheet of matching coloured paper. Make the pages into a book for the children to share with friends and family.

Bookmarks
PAGE 50

Learning objective
To make attractive bookmarks.
What to do
Work with small groups. Give each child a sheet and ask them to colour the bookmarks, drawing their favourite book character in the space provided. Let the children cut out the bookmarks. Stick a piece of wool (about 10cm long) to the back of each bookmark at the bottom. Attach a small piece of card to

the other end of the wool. Encourage the children to use the bookmarks as 'reading partners' so that they tell the story they're looking at 'to' their bookmark.

Super stories
PAGE 51

Learning objective
To express ideas and opinions about known books.
What to do
Work with small groups. Ask the children to talk about books they are familiar with and decide which ones they really like, what they are about, and why they like them. Help them to fill in the sheet and to decide upon an appropriate illustration.

Send copies of the sheet home with the children. Parents can help their child to fill in a sheet when they read and enjoy a book together.

Favourite books
PAGE 52

Learning objective
To keep a record of favourite books.
What to do
Provide each child with a sheet of their own. Discuss with them, individually, which books they have 'read', shared and enjoyed. Help them to write the title of the book. Ask them to decide upon an illustration which really describes what the book is about and to draw and colour it in the space.

Keep the sheets in the children's folders as part of their yearly reading records.

Flap book

Draw two more pictures and make your own flap book.

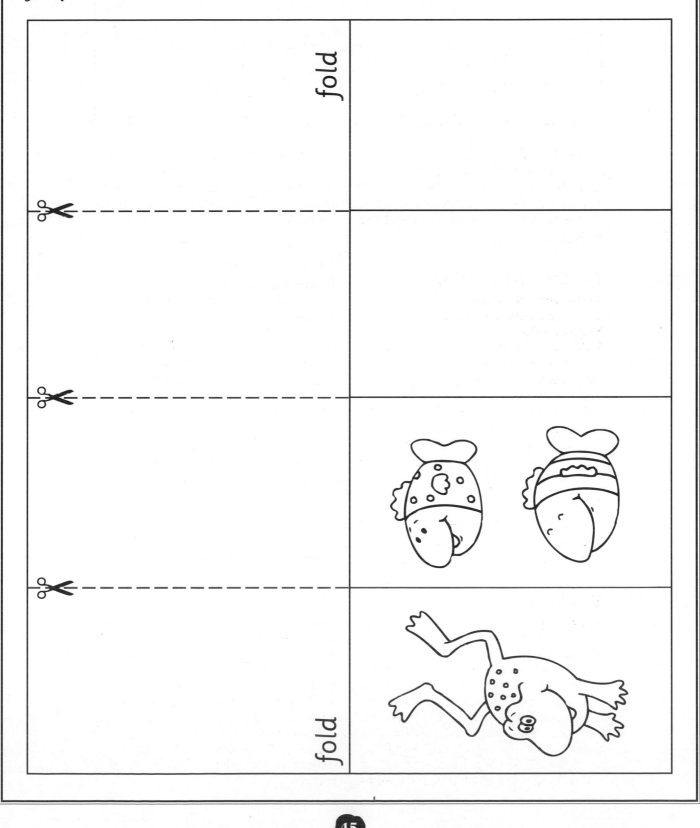

What's the story?

Put the pictures in order to tell the story.

Tell the story

Cut out the pictures and tell the story.

Butterfly

Make a pop-up book.

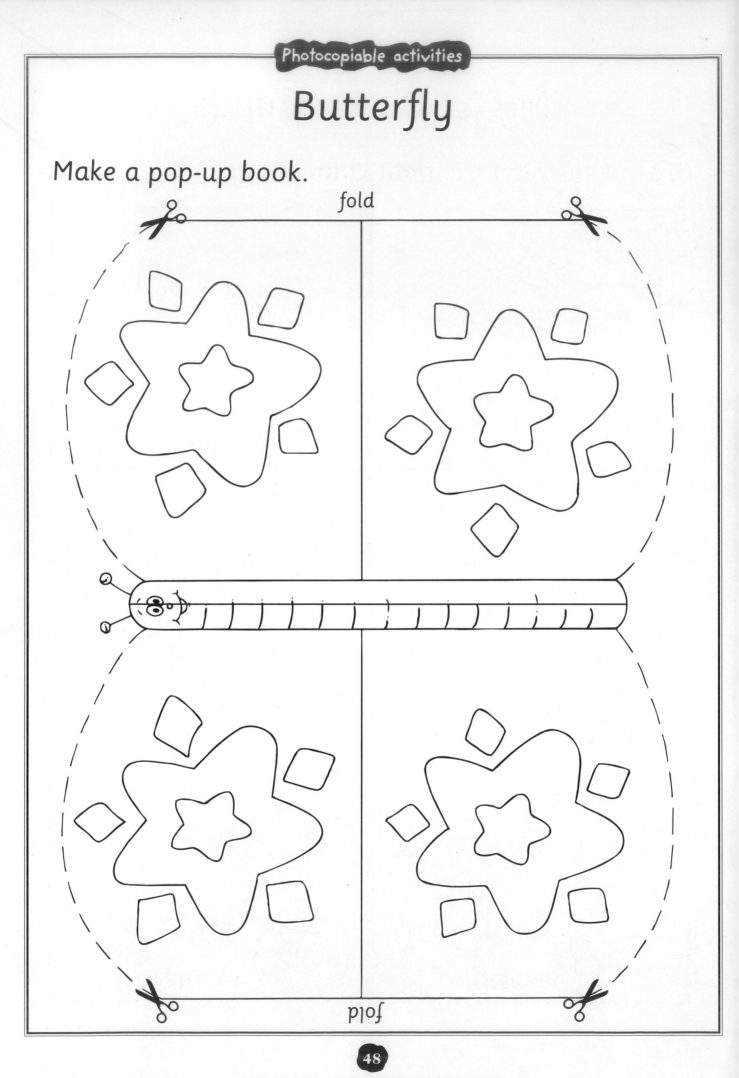

My favourite things

Draw something the right colour in each box.

red	blue
yellow	green
purple	orange

Bookmarks

Colour the bookmarks and cut them out. Draw a bookmark of your own.

Learning in the Early Years - Photocopiable Activities

Language and Literacy

Super stories

My name is _____

Title of book _____

_____

I like it because _____

_____

_____

It tells the story of _____

_____

_____

Favourite books

Language and Literacy

My name is _____

I have read

1 _____

_____

2 _____

_____

3 _____

_____

4 _____

_____

chapter five

Early writing skills

The activities in this chapter aim to provide children with the many skills needed to develop their early writing, including knowledge of some letters of the alphabet, left-to-right orientation skills and pencil control. The motivating ideas will also help the children to develop an enthusiasm for writing.

PAGE 55

Playtime

Learning objective

To practise drawing circles, taking the pencil on and off the page.

What to do

Work with up to three children, give each child a sheet. Explain that each of the children is playing with a ball, but it is invisible. Ask the children to look at the pictures and decide what sort of action they are using with their ball (such as kicking, bouncing, throwing and so on). Invite the children to draw in the balls in the appropriate places.

PAGE56

Join the shapes

Learning objective

To develop left-to-right orientation skills.

What to do

Work with up to three children. Ask the children to identify and name each shape on the page. Show them the starting point and ending point for each

pair. Ask them to draw straight lines from left to right, to join each pair. Use this technique to match pictures, letters and words.

Follow the path

PAGE 57

Learning objective

To practise control and direction of pencil line.

What to do

Work with small groups. Give each child a copy of the sheet. Ask them to find the bear and the pot of honey, these are the starting and ending points. Can they see anything else? Ask them to trace the dotted line with a finger, then trace over it with a pencil to help the bear to reach the honey.

Letter sounds

PAGE 58

Learning objective

To match letters by shape and sound.

What to do

Work with individual children. Talk about the letter in the first square, can the child recognize it? Can they say its sound? Encourage the child to trace carefully over the dotted letter. Ask them to copy the letter into the second box, and draw something beginning with its letter sound in the third box.

Repeat the process for each row. Cut the squares out and stick them to card. Mix them up and invite the child to sort them into their appropriate sets.

PAGE 59

Invitation

Learning objective
To practise writing for a purpose.
What to do
Give each child in a small group an activity sheet. Set up a 'game' of birthday party in the home corner. Invite the children to choose a character from a traditional tale to come to their 'birthday'. Help each child to fill in their invitation and decorate them with colouring materials and collage pieces. Provide envelopes for the children to use, giving them help to invent and write an address. Let them take turns to have a 'birthday party' in the home corner, using their invitations.

PAGE 60

Shopping list

Learning objective
To create a list with words or symbols.
What to do
Work with two children at a time, providing each with an activity sheet. Show them the Bear's shopping list down the left hand side. Encourage the children to name the objects illustrated around the edge of the list. Now invite each child to write their name in the space provided and help them to write or draw their own shopping list beneath. Create a shop in the role-play area and encourage the children to use the shopping lists in their play.

PAGE 61

Special today

Learning objective
To write for a specific purpose.
What to do
Work with up to three children. Give them a sheet each. Talk about 'eating out'. Where do they like to eat? What do they choose from the menu? Together, look at the menu and identify the items on offer. Help the children to write in the words. Now set up an area of the room as a café, let them take turns to be the cook, waiter/waitress and customers using the menu to make their choices.

Match the sounds

PAGE 62

Learning objectives
To match sounds and letters and to practise letter formation.
What to do
Work with small groups, giving each child an activity sheet. Look at the pictures and say the names of the objects. Trace over the letters with fingers to feel the shape and flow. Say the letter sounds together. Can they decide which letter sound goes with which picture? Let the children colour the pictures and letters. Stick the sheet to card and cut out the boxes. Use the cards for matching games.

Capital match

PAGE 63

Learning objective
To match capital and small letters.
What to do
Work with individuals or pairs. Ask the children to trace their fingers along the shapes of the letters. Do they know the names of the capital letters? Do they know the sounds of the lower case letters? Do they know which letter goes with which? Let the children colour in the letters. Stick them to card and cut them out. Can the children find the matching pairs?

Talk to the children about their own names and make letter cards of their special letters. Help them to sort the letters into the sequence of their name. Where does the capital letter go?

The big balloon

PAGE 64

Learning objective
To create and write a story.
What to do
Work with pairs of children, providing each child with a sheet. Talk about the pictures together and encourage them to make up their own ending. Let the children colour and cut out the pictures, sticking each to a separate page. Ask them to give you a sentence to describe each picture and write it underneath for them.

Now invite them to draw a picture to finish the story. Staple or tie the pages together, helping the children to make a title page. Encourage the children to share their books with friends and families.

Playtime

The children are playing. Draw five balls.

Join the shapes.

Join each shape to its partner with a straight line.

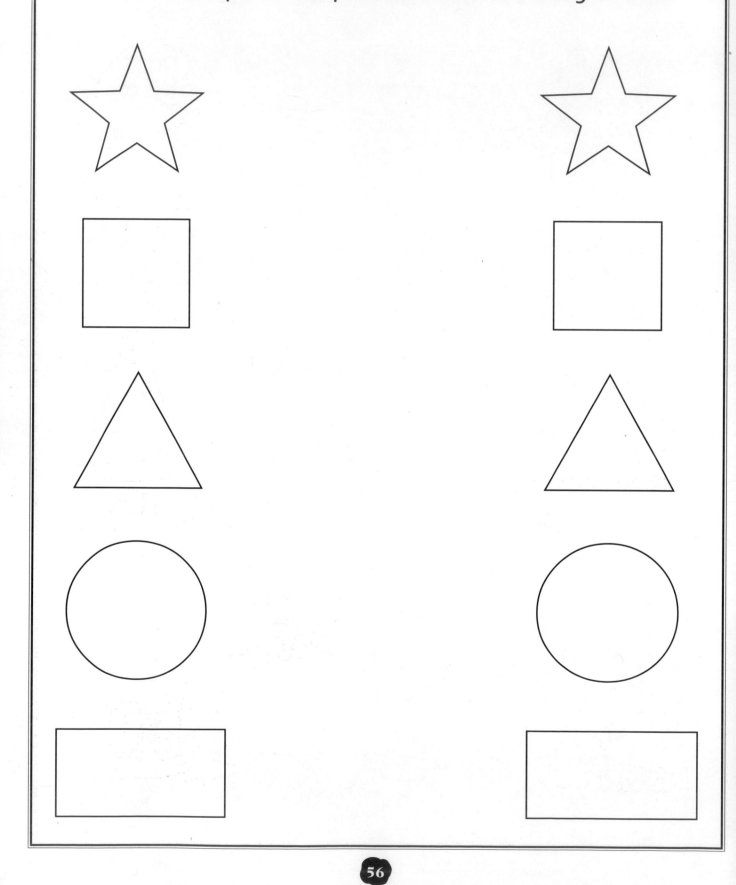

Follow the path

Help the bear to get to the honey.

Letter sounds

Trace the letter. Write the letter. Draw something that begins with its sound.

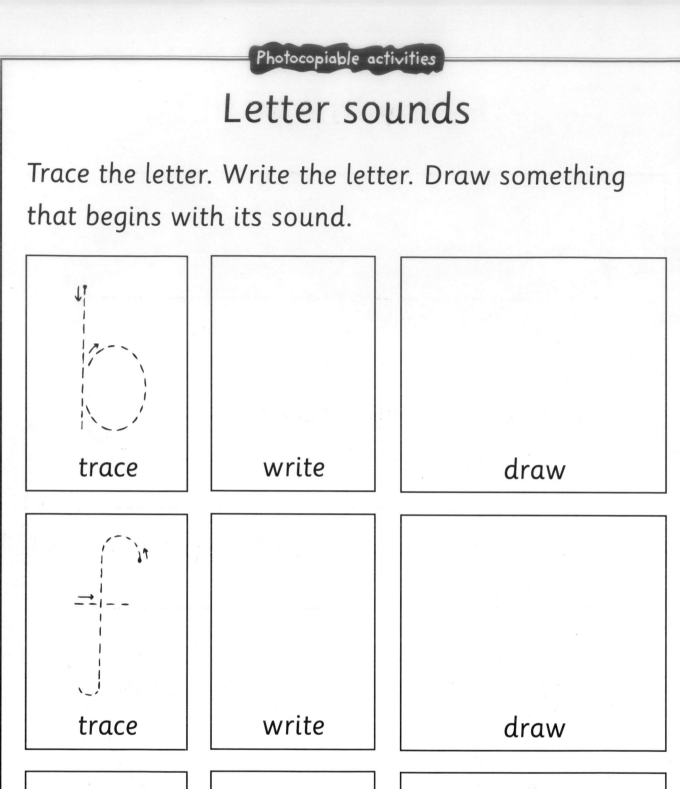

| trace | write | draw |

| trace | write | draw |

| trace | write | draw |

Invitation

Dear _____

Please come to my party on

_____

Love from _____

Shopping list

Draw or write.

Bear's
shopping list

_____
shopping list

Learning in the Early Years - Photocopiable Activities

Language and Literacy

Special today

Write the words.

Match sounds.

Which letter goes with which picture?

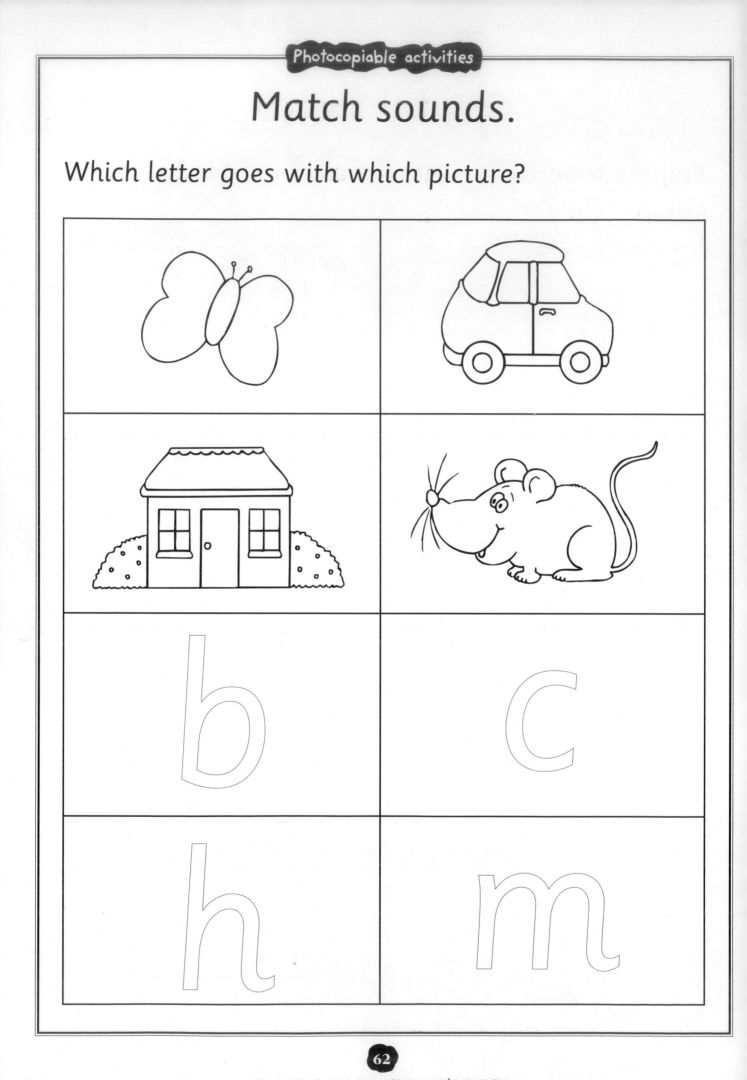

Capital match

Say the sounds. Say the names of the capital letters. Match the pairs.

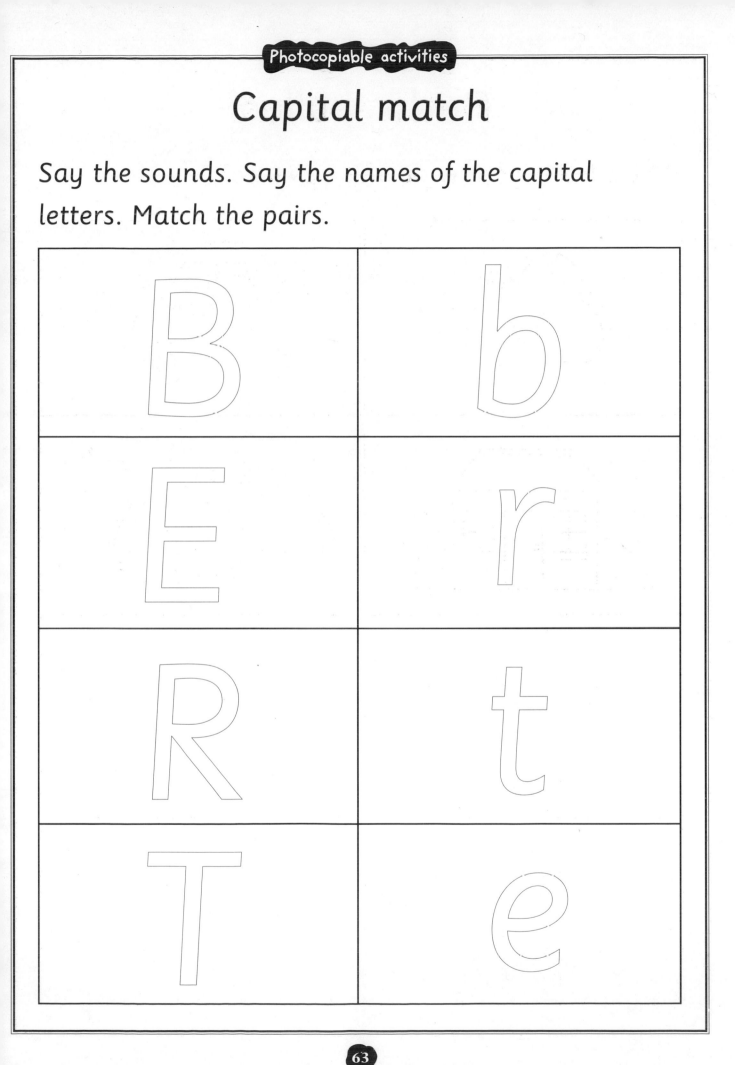

The big balloon

Tell the story. Draw a picture to finish the story.